Winter Is Here
Llegó el invierno

by Deborah Schecter

ISBN: 978-1-338-70286-6
Illustrated by Anne Kennedy
Copyright © 2020 by Deborah Schecter. All rights reserved.
Published by Scholastic Inc., 557 Broadway, New York, NY 10012

10 9 8 7 6   68   23 24 25 26/0

Printed in Jiaxing, China. First printing, June 2020.

■SCHOLASTIC

Winter is here.
Sleep, bear, sleep.

Llegó el invierno.
Duerme, oso, duerme.

Winter is here.
Sleep, snake, sleep.

Llegó el invierno.
Duerme, serpiente, duerme.

Winter is here.
Sleep, chipmunk, sleep.

Llegó el invierno.
Duerme, ardilla listada, duerme.

Winter is here.
Sleep, frog, sleep.

Llegó el invierno.
Duerme, rana, duerme.

Winter is here.
Sleep, turtle, sleep.

Llegó el invierno.
Duerme, tortuga, duerme.

Winter is here.
Sleep, groundhog, sleep.

Llegó el invierno.
Duerme, marmota, duerme.

Spring is here.
Time to wake up!

Llegó la primavera.
¡Es hora de despertar!